USBORNE FIRST READING

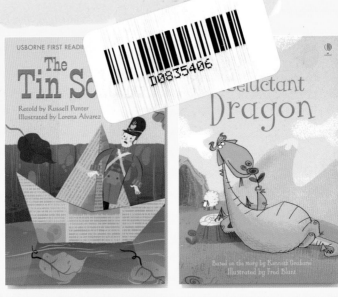

USBORNE FIRST READING

The Tin So...
Retold by Russell Punter
Illustrated by Lorena Alvarez

...eluctant **Dragon**
Based on the story by Kenneth Grahame
Illustrated by Fred Blunt

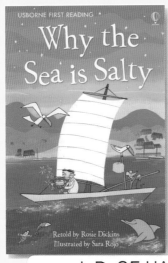

USBORNE FIRST READING

Why the Sea is Salty
Retold by Rosie Dickins
Illustrated by Sara Rojo

USBORNE FIRST READING

Thumbelina
Retold by Susanna Davidson
Illustrated by Petra Brown

THE
EASTER STORY

Retold by Russell Punter

Illustrated by John Joven

Reading consultant: Alison Kelly
University of Roehampton

Jesus lived two thousand years ago.

He went from place to place with his friends, teaching people about God's kingdom.

Once, they were on their way to Jerusalem for a festival called Passover.

They stopped at a village.

Jesus asked his friends to find him a donkey so he could ride through the city.

Jesus rode into Jerusalem,
followed by his friends.

Cheering crowds lined
the streets. Everyone was
excited to see Jesus.

It was a dusty, rough road.
People put down their cloaks
for the donkey to walk on.

Others cut leaves from palm
trees and laid them down too.

Jesus and his friends visited
the Temple to pray.

When they returned the next morning, Jesus was angry.

Traders were selling cows and other animals outside the Temple.

"This is a place for praying," said Jesus crossly. "It's not for making money."

He knocked over the traders' stalls and drove them away.

A crowd gathered. Jesus taught them about God's kingdom.

Sick people came to hear him and he made them well.

The Chief Priests of the
Temple heard about Jesus.
They decided to get rid of him.

"People should not listen to
him," said one, angrily.

"We'll arrest him," said another, "when there's no crowd around to protect him."

Judas, one of Jesus's friends, heard about the priests' plan.

"I'll tell you when Jesus is alone," he told them. "What will you give me in return?"

"Thirty silver coins," they replied.

That evening, Jesus and his friends were eating supper.

"One of you is going to betray me," said Jesus. His friends were shocked.

"It will be the man I give this bread to," Jesus added. He handed it to Judas.

Judas ran off into the night.

Jesus shared the rest of the food with his friends.

"When you eat bread and drink wine, remember me," he said.

Then Jesus went to visit a garden of olive trees nearby.

"Soon you'll run away and leave me," Jesus told his friends.

They were surprised. "We'd never do that," they said.

Jesus entered the garden with Peter, James and John. Jesus turned to Peter.

"Before the cock crows at dawn, you'll pretend you don't know me," he said.

Peter was puzzled.
"I'd never do that."

Jesus went to a quiet spot to pray alone. When he returned, his friends were asleep.

At that moment, Judas
appeared with a group of
Temple guards.

Judas kissed Jesus on
the cheek.

Peter sprang to defend Jesus
with his sword.

"Put your sword down,
Peter," said Jesus, healing
the guard.

The guards grabbed Jesus.
His friends ran off in fear.

Jesus was marched to the
High Priest's palace.

25

Peter joined a crowd outside.
"Weren't you Jesus's friend?"
asked a girl.

Peter didn't want to be
arrested. "Oh no," he lied.

Two more people asked the same question. Peter lied to them too.

The cock crowed. Peter remembered what Jesus had said earlier and cried.

Inside the palace, Jesus
stood before the High Priest.

"Are you the Son of God?"
asked the priest.
"I am," said Jesus.

"No one is allowed to say that," said the priest. "The law says you must die."

Only the Roman Governor could order Jesus's death.

29

The next morning, Jesus was taken to the Governor, Pontius Pilate.

There was a crowd outside the Governor's home.

The priests had lots of friends in the crowd. They told them to shout "Kill Jesus!"

Pilate looked down at the crowd.

He knew Jesus had done nothing wrong. But he didn't want to upset the Chief Priests.

"Very well," Pilate told the crowd. "But you must take the blame for Jesus's death."

Soldiers took Jesus and made fun of him. They dressed him in a purple robe and put a crown of thorns on his head.

Dressed in his old clothes again, Jesus was led to a wooden cross.

"You'll be put on this cross to die," said one soldier.

"Carry it outside the city first," ordered another.

The cross was very heavy.
After a while, Jesus fell down,
exhausted.

A man named Simon
saw what had happened.

The soldiers made Simon
carry the cross for Jesus. Soon,
they were beyond the city.

The soldiers hung
Jesus on the cross, as
a crowd watched.

"Forgive them, Father," prayed Jesus. "They don't know what they're doing."

That afternoon, Jesus died.

At that moment, the
ground shook.

"He really must have been
the Son of God," said the
soldier in charge.

A man named Joseph
took away Jesus's body. He
wrapped it in a linen cloth.

Joseph and some of Jesus's friends took the body to a garden.

They laid the body gently inside a tomb.

Then, they rolled a huge
stone in front of the tomb.

By this time, it was late on
Friday evening.

Three of Jesus's friends returned on Sunday. They were astonished.

The stone had been moved and Jesus's body was gone.

A man appeared, dressed in white. "Do not be afraid," he said. "Jesus is alive."

The women ran to tell Jesus's other friends what had happened.

45

Later, one woman, Mary,
came back by herself.
Suddenly, Jesus appeared.

"Tell my friends you've seen
me, Mary," he said.

After that, Jesus's friends saw him several times before he went to Heaven.

They told everyone about Jesus. Now they knew he would live forever.

Text consultant: Clare Mitchell
Designed by Caroline Spatz
Digital manipulation by Nick Wakeford
Series editor: Lesley Sims

First published in 2013 by Usborne Publishing Ltd., Usborne House,
83-85 Saffron Hill, London EC1N 8RT, England. www.usborne.com
Copyright © 2013 Usborne Publishing Ltd.

48